365

ways to live in harmony

365

ways to live in harmony

**COLORING AND
WISDOM TO LIFT
YOUR SPIRITS**

vmb
PUBLISHERS

INTRODUCTION

The frantic tempo of life is stressful, with daily tasks and pressing deadlines accumulating day after day. It's no wonder many want to escape to nature or find solace in even a momentary break for a cup of tea. Art therapy is also a means to relaxation. Coloring the pages of this book will engage the mind in an enjoyable, creative activity that is highly satisfying.

Nature, with its fresh and reassuring colors, its harmonious and amazing forms, its peaceful and unchangeable rhythm, is relaxing. It invites reflection and restores our spirit. It's not always easy, however, to find time to walk in the woods or explore a park. This wonderful illustrated book, consequently, comes to the rescue. The pages of this volume present splendid, elegant illustrations of nature – from fields full of flowers to sinuous fish and birds inhabiting tropical paradises.

But wildlife isn't the only subject available. Here we also find the nature of interiors: an object of daily use – a teapot, a pair of shoes, or a grandfather clock – can come to life thanks to the marvelous details composing the image. By committing yourself to the act of coloring, according to your personal taste and imagination, you benefit from the positive spirit of artistic activity.

There are no limits to the imagination. Once you have chosen whether to use crayons or felt-tip pens and select your color preferences, the illustrations in the

following pages will become an expression of your aesthetic taste. Animals, flowers, and plants will come to life in a kaleidoscope of fantastic shades illuminated by your imagination. Technical ability is no concern. Art therapy is within reach for everyone. You will obtain amazing results that your friends will love and admire.

Besides coloring the drawings, you will be able to read the 365 quotations from famous figures. There is an aphorism for every day of the year from philosophers, people of faith, Hollywood celebrities, literary figures, scientists, and elder statesmen. This precious collection of maxims and thoughts provides inspiration to face each day with the right attitude and peace of mind. At the end of this journey of 365 days, you will find that you have completed a route that, thanks to the colors of nature and the opportunities of introspection, has relaxed you as well as made you stronger and more self-aware.

1

"Be happy for this moment.
This moment is your life."

– Omar Khayyam

2

"A contented mind is the greatest
blessing a man can enjoy
in this world."

– Joseph Addison

3

"The best way to pay for a lovely
moment is to enjoy it."

– *Richard Bach*

4

"Color is my day-long obsession,
joy and torment."

– Claude Monet

5

"Joy is prayer; joy is strength: joy is love;
joy is a net of love by which you
can catch souls."

– Mother Teresa of Calcutta

6

"Happiness is like a cloud, if you stare
at it long enough, it evaporates."

– Sarah McLachlan

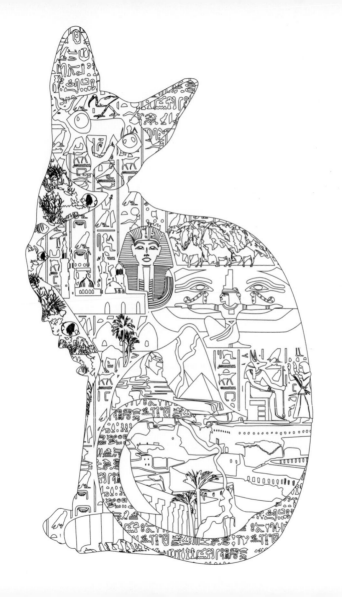

7

"Painting is just another way
of keeping a diary."

– Pablo Picasso

8

"If you do what you love,
it is the best way to relax."

– Christian Louboutin

9

"Enlightenment is always there. Small
enlightenment will bring great enlightenment.
If you breathe in and are aware that you are alive -
that you can touch the miracle of being alive -
then that is a kind of enlightenment."

– Thich Nhat Hanh

10

"Happiness is when what you think, what
you say, and what you do are in harmony."

– Mahatma Gandhi

11

"Every painting is a voyage
into a sacred harbor."

– Giotto

12

"Find a place inside where there's joy,
and the joy will burn out the pain."

– Joseph Campbell

13

"Happiness... consists in giving,
and in serving others."

– Henry Drummond

14

"One of the most beautiful qualities
of true friendship is to understand
and to be understood."

– Lucius Annaeus Seneca

15

"Keep close to Nature's heart... and break clear away,
once in awhile, and climb a mountain or spend a week
in the woods. Wash your spirit clean."

– John Muir

16

"A smile is a curve that sets
everything straight."

– Phyllis Diller

17

"No pessimist ever discovered the secret of
the stars, or sailed to an uncharted land, or
opened a new doorway for the human spirit."

– Helen Keller

18

"Some painters transform the sun into a yellow
spot, others transform a yellow spot into the sun."

– Pablo Picasso

19

"It is not how much we have, but how much we enjoy, that makes happiness."

– Charles Spurgeon

20

"Joy in looking and comprehending is nature's most beautiful gift."

– Albert Einstein

21

"Green is the prime color of the world, and that from which its loveliness arises."

– Pedro Calderon de la Barca

22

"Everything has beauty,
but not everyone sees it."

– Confucius

23

"Nature always wears the colors
of the spirit."

– Ralph Waldo Emerson

24

"Joy is the simplest form of gratitude."

– Karl Barth

25

"With an eye made quiet by the power
of harmony, and the deep power of joy,
we see into the life of things."

– William Wordsworth

26

"The most glorious moments in your life
are not the so-called days of success,
but rather those days when out of dejection
and despair you feel rise in you a challenge to life,
and the promise of future accomplishments."

– Gustave Flaubert

27

"Don't walk in front of me, I may not follow.
Don't walk behind me, I may not lead.
There is only one happiness in life,
to love and be loved."

– George Sand

28

"Nature does nothing in vain."

– Aristotle

29

"There is nothing on this earth more
to be prized than true friendship."

– Saint Thomas Aquinas

30

"Since love grows within you, so beauty grows. For love is the beauty of the soul."

– Saint Augustine

31

"The person who can bring the spirit of laughter into a room is indeed blessed."

– Bennett Cerf

32

"Happiness is the spiritual experience of living every minute with love, grace, and gratitude."

– *Denis Waitley*

33

"No one undertakes research in physics with the intention of winning a prize. It is the joy of discovering something no one knew before."

– Stephen Hawking

34

"Painting is silent poetry, and poetry is painting that speaks."

– Plutarch

35

"The real meaning of enlightenment is to gaze with undimmed eyes on all darkness."

– Nikos Kazantzakis

36

"Your mind will answer most questions if
you learn to relax and wait for the answer."

– William S. Burroughs

37

"Rest when you're weary. Refresh and
renew yourself, your body, your mind,
your spirit. Then get back to work."

– Ralph Marston

38

"A warm smile is the universal
language of kindness."

– *William Arthur Ward*

39

"I don't think of all the misery
but of the beauty that still remains."

– Anne Frank

40

"Luck is not chance, it's toil; fortune's
expensive smile is earned."

– Emily Dickinson

41

"A happy life must be to a great extent
a quiet life, for it is only in an atmosphere
of quiet that true joy dare live."

– Bertrand Russell

42

"We do not see nature with our eyes, but
with our understandings and our hearts."

– *William Hazlitt*

43

"The good man is the friend
of all living things."

– Mahatma Gandhi

44

"Every gift from a friend is a wish
for your happiness."

– Richard Bach

45

"Some people walk in the rain,
others just get wet."

– Roger Miller

46

"To be stupid, selfish, and have good health
are three requirements for happiness, though
if stupidity is lacking, all is lost."

– Gustave Flaubert

47

"Kind words do not cost much.
Yet they accomplish much."

– Blaise Pascal

48

"Each day provides its own gifts."

– Marcus Aurelius

49

"I do not know whether I was then a man dreaming I was a butterfly, or whether I am now a butterfly dreaming I am a man."

– Zhuangzi

50

"There is no pain so great as the memory of joy in present grief."

– Aeschylus

51

"You should feel beautiful and you should feel safe. What you surround yourself with should bring you peace of mind and peace of spirit."

– Stacy London

52

"Your spirit is the true shield."

– Morihei Ueshiba

53

"The two enemies of human happiness
are pain and boredom."

– Arthur Schopenhauer

54

"Ah, lives of men! When prosperous
they glitter - Like a fair picture; when
misfortune comes - A wet sponge at one
blow has blurred the painting."

– Aeschylus

55

"Nature provides exceptions to every rule."

– *Margaret Fuller*

56

"Let us always meet each other with a
smile, for the smile is the beginning of love."

– *Mother Teresa of Calcutta*

57

"There are only two forces in the world,
the sword and the spirit. In the long run the
sword will always be conquered by the spirit."

– *Napoleon Bonaparte*

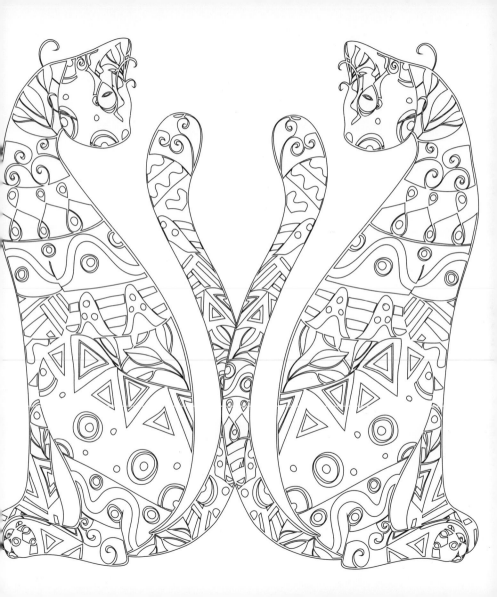

58

"Sculpture is the best comment that a painter can make on painting."

– Pablo Picasso

59

"If you wait for the perfect moment when all is safe and assured,
it may never arrive. Mountains will not be climbed, races won,
or lasting happiness achieved."

– Maurice Chevalier

60

"It is the supreme art of the teacher to awaken joy in creative expression
and knowledge."

– Albert Einstein

61

"It is only with the heart that one can see
rightly; what is essential is invisible to the eye."

— *Antoine de Saint-Exupéry*

62

"I can resist everything except temptation."

— *Oscar Wilde*

63

"From a little spark may burst a flame."

— *Dante Alighieri*

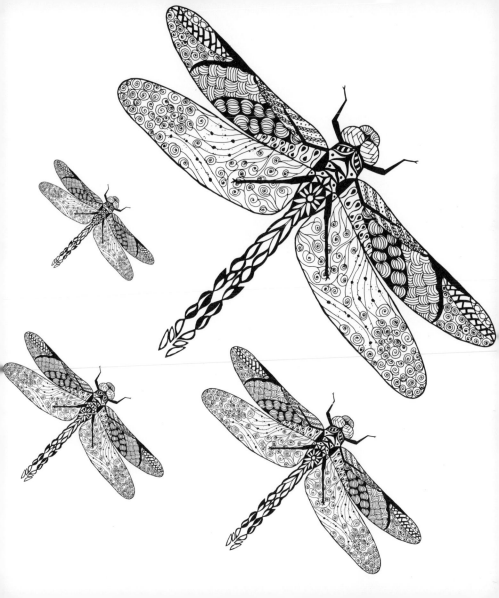

64

"Success is a consequence
and must not be a goal."

– *Gustave Flaubert*

65

"Do not dwell in the past, do not dream of
the future, concentrate the mind on the
present moment."

– *Buddha*

66

"Happiness can exist only in acceptance."

– *George Orwell*

67

"Don't wait around for other people to be happy for you. Any happiness you get you've got to make yourself."

– Alice Walker

68

"If the sight of the blue skies fills you with joy, if a blade of grass springing up in the fields has power to move you, if the simple things of nature have a message that you understand, rejoice, for your soul is alive."

– Eleonora Duse

69

"Love is the joy of the good, the wonder of the wise, the amazement of the gods."

– Plato

70

"It is requisite for the relaxation of the mind
that we make use, from time to time,
of playful deeds and jokes."

– Saint Thomas Aquinas

71

"For in the true nature of things, if we rightly
consider, every green tree is far more glorious
than if it were made of gold and silver."

— *Martin Luther*

72

"To enjoy good health, to bring true happiness
to one's family, to bring peace to all, one must
first discipline and control one's own mind.
If a man can control his mind he can find the
way to Enlightenment, and all wisdom and
virtue will naturally come to him."

– Buddha

73

"A real friend is one who walks in
when the rest of the world walks out."

– Walter Winchell

74

"Let us be grateful to people who make
us happy, they are the charming gardeners
who make our souls blossom."

– Marcel Proust

75

"In everyone's life, at some time, our inner fire goes out. It is then burst into flame by an encounter with another human being. We should all be thankful for those people who rekindle the inner spirit."

– Albert Schweitzer

76

"Let my soul smile through my heart and my heart smile through my eyes, that I may scatter rich smiles in sad hearts."

– Paramahansa Yogananda

77

"In life, as in art, the beautiful moves in curves."

– Edward G. Bulwer-Lytton

78

"Throughout the time in which I am working on a canvas I can feel how I am beginning to love it, with that love which is born of slow comprehension."

– *Joan Miró*

79

"Nature holds the key to our aesthetic, intellectual, cognitive and even spiritual satisfaction."

– *E. O. Wilson*

80

"Love is the attempt to form a friendship inspired by beauty."

– *Marcus Tullius Cicero*

81

"If one way be better than another,
that you may be sure is nature's way."

— *Aristotle*

82

"Imagination decides everything."

— *Blaise Pascal*

83

"Iron rusts from disuse; water loses its
purity from stagnation... even so does
inaction sap the vigor of the mind."

— *Leonardo da Vinci*

84

"Just do what must be done. This may not be happiness,
but it is greatness."

– George Bernard Shaw

85

"Basically, at the very bottom of life, which seduces us all, there is only
absurdity, and more absurdity. And maybe that's what gives us our joy
for living, because the only thing that can defeat absurdity is lucidity."

– Albert Camus

86

"Not creating delusions is enlightenment."

– Bodhidharma

87

"Loyalty and devotion lead to bravery.
Bravery leads to the spirit of self-
sacrifice. The spirit of self-sacrifice
creates trust in the power of love."

– Morihei Ueshiba

"A gentle word, a kind look, a good-
natured smile can work wonders
and accomplish miracles."

– *William Hazlitt*

89

"Flowers... are a proud assertion that a ray of
beauty outvalues all the utilities of the world."

– Ralph Waldo Emerson

90

"We are no longer happy so soon
as we wish to be happier."

– Walter Savage Landor

91

"When I look back at that freedom of
childhood, which is in a way infinite, and at
all the joy and the intense happiness, now
lost, I sometimes think that childhood is
where the real meaning of life is located, and
that we, adults, are its servants - that that's
our purpose."

– Karl Ove Knausgaard

92

"A smile is the light in your window that tells others
that there is a caring, sharing person inside."

– Denis Waitley

93

"True happiness is... to enjoy the present, without anxious
dependence upon the future."

– Lucius Annaeus Seneca

94

"Find joy in everything you choose to do. Every job, relationship,
home... it's your responsibility to love it, or change it."

– Chuck Palahniuk

95

"I dream of painting and then I paint my dream."

– Vincent van Gogh

96

"We need enlightenment, not just individually
but collectively, to save the planet. We need
to awaken ourselves. We need to practice
mindfulness if we want to have a future,
if we want to save ourselves and the planet."

– Thich Nhat Hanh

97

"Friends are the siblings God never gave us."

– Mencius

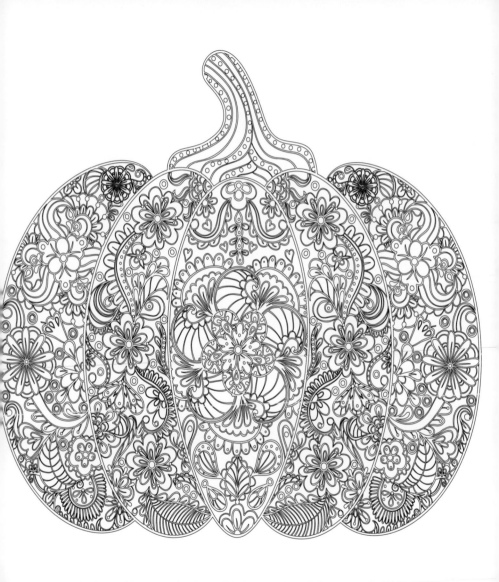

98

"All theory, dear friend, is gray, but the golden tree of life springs ever green."

– *Johann Wolfgang von Goethe*

99

"Friendship is always a sweet responsibility, never an opportunity."

– *Khalil Gibran*

100

"Never be in a hurry; do everything quietly and in a calm spirit. Do not lose your inner peace for anything whatsoever, even if your whole world seems upset."

– *Saint Francis de Sales*

101

"The virtues, like the Muses, are always seen in groups.
A good principle was never found solitary in any breast."

– Buddha

102

"Nothing can cure the soul but the senses, just as nothing
can cure the senses but the soul."

– Oscar Wilde

103

"The meaning of things lies not in the things themselves,
but in our attitude towards them."

– Antoine de Saint-Exupéry

104

"We sail within a vast sphere, ever drifting
in uncertainty, driven from end to end."

– Blaise Pascal

105

"When nature has work to be done,
she creates a genius to do it."

– Ralph Waldo Emerson

106

"Twilight drops her curtain down,
and pins it with a star."

– Lucy Maud Montgomery

107

"Land really is the best art."

– Andy Warhol

108

"Happiness cannot be traveled to, owned,
earned, worn or consumed."

– Denis Waitley

109

"I, not events, have the power to make
me happy or unhappy today. I can choose
which it shall be. Yesterday is dead,
tomorrow hasn't arrived yet. I have just one
day, today, and I'm going to be happy in it."

– Groucho Marx

110

"The pain of parting is nothing
to the joy of meeting again."

– Charles Dickens

111

"Painting is concerned with all the 10
attributes of sight; which are: Darkness,
Light, Solidity and Color, Form and
Position, Distance and Propinquity,
Motion and Rest."

– Leonardo da Vinci

112

"To describe happiness is to diminish it."

– Stendhal

113

"I used to live in a room full of mirrors; all I could see was me. I take my spirit and I crash my mirrors, now the whole world is here for me to see."

— Jimi Hendrix

114

"If you nurture your mind, body, and spirit, your time will expand. You will gain a new perspective that will allow you to accomplish much more."

— Brian Koslow

115

"Don't cry because it's over. Smile because it happened."

— Dr. Seuss

116

"The best part of beauty is that which no picture can express."

– Francis Bacon

117

"The butterfly counts not months but moments, and has time enough."

– Rabindranath Tagore

118

"Forget not that the earth delights to feel
your bare feet and the winds long to play
with your hair."

– Khalil Gibran

119

"Anything becomes interesting
if you look at it long enough."

– Gustave Flaubert

120

"The world of reality has its limits;
the world of imagination is boundless."

– Jean-Jacques Rousseau

121

"Nowhere can man find a quieter or more untroubled retreat than in his own soul."

– Marcus Aurelius

122

"If a man insisted always on being serious, and never allowed himself a bit of fun and relaxation, he would go mad or become unstable without knowing it."

– Herodotus

123

"Lend your ears to music, open your eyes to painting, and... stop thinking! Just ask yourself whether the work has enabled you to 'walk about' into a hitherto unknown world. If the answer is yes, what more do you want?"

– Wassily Kandinsky

124

"Youth is not a time of life; it is a state of mind; it is not a matter of rosy cheeks, red lips and supple knees; it is a matter of the will, quality of the imagination, a vigor of the emotions; it is the freshness of the deep springs of life."

– Samuel Ullman

125

"Those who are free of resentful thoughts
surely find peace."

– Buddha

126

"Happiness is like a kiss.
You must share it to enjoy it."

– Bernard Meltzer

127

"A sense of humor... is needed armor. Joy in
one's heart and some laughter on one's lips is
a sign that the person down deep has a pretty
good grasp of life."

– Hugh Sidey

128

"Love is the only force capable of transforming an enemy into a friend."

– Martin Luther King, Jr.

129

"Friends show their love in times of trouble, not in happiness."

– Euripides

130

"We must become bigger than we have been: more courageous, greater in spirit, larger in outlook. We must become members of a new race, overcoming petty prejudice, owing our ultimate allegiance not to nations but to our fellow men within the human community."

– Haile Selassie

131

"Hate is always a clash between our spirit
and someone else's body."

– Cesare Pavese

132

"There is the sky,
which is all men's together."

– Euripides

133

"Reality does not conform to the ideal,
but confirms it."

– Gustave Flaubert

134

"The only wealth which you will keep
forever is the wealth you have given away."

– *Marcus Aurelius*

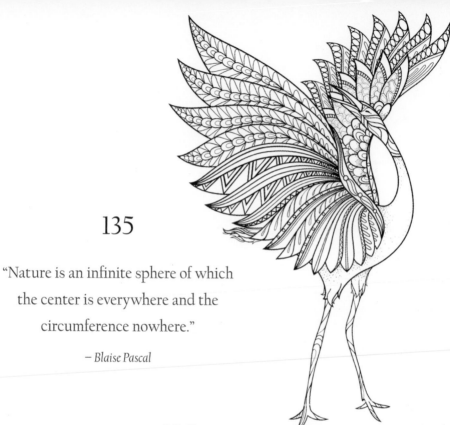

135

"Nature is an infinite sphere of which
the center is everywhere and the
circumference nowhere."

– *Blaise Pascal*

136

"It is better to travel well than to arrive."

– *Buddha*

137

"The garden of love is green without limit
and yields many fruits other than sorrow
or joy. Love is beyond either condition:
without spring, without autumn, it is
always fresh."

– Rumi

138

"Nobody understands another's sorrow,
and nobody another's joy."

– Franz Schubert

139

"A sure way to lose happiness, I found, is to
want it at the expense of everything else."

– Bette Davis

140

"Be happy with what you have and are,
be generous with both, and you won't have
to hunt for happiness."

– William E. Gladstone

141

"Man cannot live without joy; therefore when he is deprived of true spiritual joys it is necessary that he become addicted to carnal pleasures."

– Saint Thomas Aquinas

142

"It is a fine seasoning for joy
to think of those we love."

– *Molière*

143

"No one is an artist unless he carries
his picture in his head before painting it,
and is sure of his method and composition."

– *Claude Monet*

144

"Who will tell whether one happy moment
of love or the joy of breathing or walking
on a bright morning and smelling the fresh
air, is not worth all the suffering and effort
which life implies."

– *Erich Fromm*

145

"A friend is, as it were, a second self."

– Marcus Tullius Cicero

146

"The love is fixed, instantly accessible to memory, somehow stained into my body as color into cloth."

– Anne Truitt

147

"While the laughter of joy is in full harmony
with our deeper life, the laughter of
amusement should be kept apart from it.
The danger is too great of thus learning to look
at solemn things in a spirit of mockery, and to
seek in them opportunities for exercising wit."

– Lewis Carroll

148

"Everybody needs beauty as well as bread,
places to play in and pray in, where nature
may heal and give strength to body and soul."

– John Muir

149

"Where the spirit does not work with
the hand, there is no art."

– Leonardo da Vinci

150

"The experience of life consists of the experience which the spirit has of itself in matter and as matter, in mind and as mind, in emotion, as emotion, etc."

– Franz Kafka

151

"Imagination disposes of everything; it creates beauty, justice, and happiness, which are everything in this world."

– Blaise Pascal

152

"Human life is as evanescent as the morning dew or a flash of lightning."

– Samuel Butler

153

"Little things console us because
little things afflict us."

– *Blaise Pascal*

154

"What is the beautiful, if not the impossible."

– *Gustave Flaubert*

155

"The happiness of your life depends upon
the quality of your thoughts: therefore,
guard accordingly, and take care that you
entertain no notions unsuitable to virtue
and reasonable nature."

– Marcus Aurelius

156

"Follow your own star!"

– Dante Alighieri

157

"You, yourself, as much as anybody
in the entire universe, deserve your
love and affection."

– Buddha

158

"Plenty of people miss their share of happiness, not because they never found it, but because they didn't stop to enjoy it."

– William Feather

159

"Achievement of your happiness is the only moral purpose of your life, and that happiness, not pain or mindless self-indulgence, is the proof of your moral integrity, since it is the proof and the result of your loyalty to the achievement of your values."

– Ayn Rand

160

"Happiness often sneaks
in through a door you didn't
know you left open."

– *John Barrymore*

161

"To live happily is an inward power of the soul."

– Marcus Aurelius

162

"Red is such an interesting color to correlate with emotion, because it's on both ends of the spectrum. On one end you have happiness, falling in love, infatuation with someone, passion, all that. On the other end, you've got obsession, jealousy, danger, fear, anger and frustration."

– Taylor Swift

163

"To be able to throw one's self away for the sake of a moment, to be able to sacrifice years for a woman's smile - that is happiness."

– Hermann Hesse

164

"The man who makes everything that leads to happiness
depends upon himself, and not upon other men, has adopted
the very best plan for living happily. This is the man of
moderation, the man of manly character and of wisdom."

– Plato

165

"Joy's smile is much closer to tears
than laughter."

– Victor Hugo

166

"Balance, peace, and joy are the fruit of a successful life.
It starts with recognizing your talents and finding ways
to serve others by using them."

– Thomas Kinkade

167

"An optimist is a person who sees a green light everywhere, while a pessimist sees only the red stoplight... the truly wise person is colorblind."

– *Albert Schweitzer*

168

"Love is a chain of love as nature is a chain of life."

– *Truman Capote*

169

"Don't walk behind me; I may not lead. Don't walk in front of me; I may not follow. Just walk beside me and be my friend."

– *Albert Camus*

170

"The greatest enemy to human souls
is the self-righteous spirit which makes
men look to themselves for salvation."

– Charles Spurgeon

171

"A spirit of innovation is generally the result of
a selfish temper and confined views. People will
not look forward to posterity, who never look
backward to their ancestors."

– Edmund Burke

172

"True happiness... is not attained
through self-gratification, but through
fidelity to a worthy purpose."

– Helen Keller

173

"It is neither wealth nor splendor;
but tranquility and occupation which
give you happiness."

– Thomas Jefferson

174

"Joy descends gently upon us like
the evening dew, and does not patter
down like a hailstorm."

– Jean Paul

175

"The spirit of envy can destroy;
it can never build."

– Margaret Thatcher

176

"Some cause happiness wherever they go;
others whenever they go."

– *Oscar Wilde*

177

"Human nature is not black and
white but black and grey."

– *Graham Greene*

178

"You must try to generate happiness within yourself.
If you aren't happy in one place, chances are you
won't be happy anyplace."

– Ernie Banks

179

"Wilderness is not a luxury
but a necessity of the human spirit."

– Edward Abbey

180

"Art is contemplation. It is the pleasure of the mind which searches into
nature and which there divines the spirit of which nature herself is animated."

– Auguste Rodin

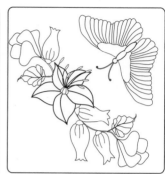

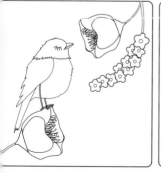

181

"They might not need me; but they might. I'll let my head be just in sight; a smile as small as mine might be precisely their necessity."

– Emily Dickinson

182

"Beauty is a fragile gift."

– Ovid

183

"The soul becomes dyed with the color of its thoughts."

– Marcus Aurelius

184

"What we think, we become."

– Buddha

185

"We are all different. There is no such thing as a standard or run-of-the-mill human being, but we share the same human spirit."

– Stephen Hawking

186

"To make a prairie it takes a clover and one bee – one clover, and a bee, and revery. The revery alone will do, if bees are few."

– Emily Dickinson

187

"The supreme function of reason is to show
man that some things are beyond reason."

– Blaise Pascal

188

"Execute every act of thy life
as though it were thy last."

— Marcus Aurelius

189

"Happiness is the absence
of the striving for happiness."

– *Zhuangzi*

190

"He is richest who is content with the least,
for content is the wealth of nature."

– *Socrates*

191

"For my part I know nothing with
any certainty, but the sight of the stars
makes me dream."

– Vincent van Gogh

192

"The poetry of the earth is never dead."

– John Keats

193

"The first recipe for happiness is:
avoid too lengthy meditation on the past."

– André Maurois

194

"If you're not having a good time,
find something else that gives
you some joy in life."

– Penny Marshall

195

"Eloquence is a painting
of the thoughts."

– Blaise Pascal

196

"Beauty, sweet love, is like the morning
dew, whose short refresh upon tender
green, cheers for a time, but till the
sun doth show and straight is gone,
as it had never been."

– Samuel Daniel

197

"Health is the greatest possession.
Contentment is the greatest treasure.
Confidence is the greatest friend.
Non-being is the greatest joy."

– Lao Tzu

198

"Nothing but heaven itself is better
than a friend who is really a friend."

– Plautus

199

"One touch of nature makes
the whole world kin."

– William Shakespeare

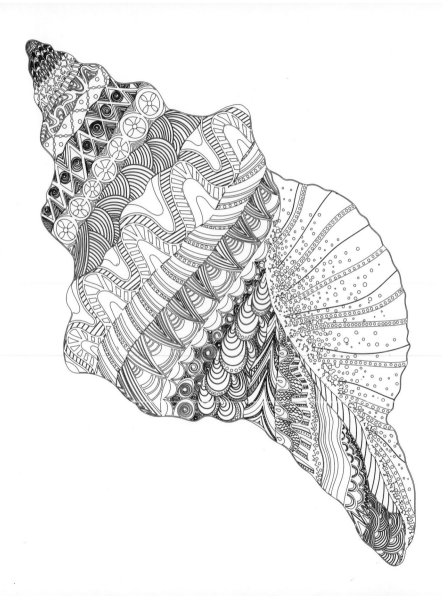

200

"Man is but a reed, the most feeble thing
in nature, but he is a thinking reed."

– *Blaise Pascal*

201

"Light in Nature creates
the movement of colors."

– *Robert Delaunay*

202

"Beauty awakens the soul to act."

– *Dante Alighieri*

203

"Three things cannot be long hidden:
the sun, the moon, and the truth."

– Buddha

204

"Happiness is not a matter of intensity
but of balance, order, rhythm
and harmony."

– Thomas Merton

205

"Some days are just bad days, that's all.
You have to experience sadness to know
happiness, and I remind myself that not
every day is going to be a good day,
that's just the way it is!"

– Dita Von Teese

206

"Life is full of happiness and tears;
be strong and have faith."

– Kareena Kapoor Khan

207

"The sun does not shine for a few trees
and flowers, but for the wide world's joy."

– Henry Ward Beecher

208

"There is joy in work. There is no happiness except in the realization that we have accomplished something."

— Henry Ford

209

"What saves a man is to take a step. Then another step. It is always the same step, but you have to take it."

— Antoine de Saint-Exupéry

210

"Pick a flower on Earth and you move the farthest star."

— Paul Dirac

211

"The sun, with all those planets revolving around it
and dependent on it, can still ripen a bunch of grapes
as if it had nothing else in the universe to do."

– Galileo Galilei

212

"Since there is nothing so well worth having as friends,
never lose a chance to make them."

– Francesco Guicciardini

213

"Happiness in intelligent people
is the rarest thing I know."

– Ernest Hemingway

214

"There are people who can do all fine and
heroic things but one - keep from telling
their happiness to the unhappy."

– Mark Twain

215

"Friendship improves happiness and abates
misery, by the doubling of our joy and the
dividing of our grief."

– Marcus Tullius Cicero

216

"Come forth into the light of things,
let nature be your teacher."

– *William Wordsworth*

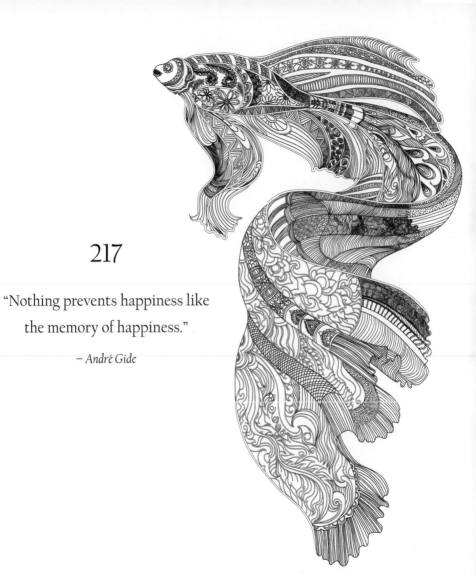

217

"Nothing prevents happiness like
the memory of happiness."

— *André Gide*

218

"Let us never know what old age is. Let us know the happiness time brings, not count the years."

– Ausonius

219

"Only by joy and sorrow does a person know anything about themselves and their destiny. They learn what to do and what to avoid."

– Johann Wolfgang von Goethe

220

"Bright reds - scarlet, pillar-box red, crimson or cherry - are very cheerful and youthful. There is certainly a red for everyone."

– Christian Dior

221

"In the sweetness of friendship let there
be laughter, and sharing of pleasures.
For in the dew of little things the heart
finds its morning and is refreshed."

– Khalil Gibran

222

"I never considered a difference of opinion in
politics, in religion, in philosophy, as cause for
withdrawing from a friend."

– Thomas Jefferson

223

"Never contract friendship
with a man that is not
better than thyself."

— *Confucius*

224

"If you are happy, you can give happiness. If you don't love yourself and if you are unhappy with yourself, you can't give anything else but that."

– Gisele Bundchen

225

"It is not so much for its beauty that the forest makes a claim upon men's hearts, as for that subtle something, that quality of air that emanation from old trees, that so wonderfully changes and renews a weary spirit."

– Robert Louis Stevenson

226

"Joy can only be real if people look upon their life as a service and have a definite object in life outside themselves and their personal happiness."

– Leo Tolstoy

227

"Desire and force between them are
responsible for all our actions; desire causes
our voluntary acts, force our involuntary."

– Blaise Pascal

228

"Begin - to begin is half the work,
let half still remain; again begin this,
and thou wilt have finished."

– Marcus Aurelius

229

"Always forgive your enemies -
nothing annoys them so much."

– Oscar Wilde

230

"My soul can find no staircase to Heaven
unless it be through Earth's loveliness."

– Michelangelo

231

"Happiness is a butterfly, which when
pursued, is always just beyond your grasp,
but which, if you will sit down quietly,
may alight upon you."

– Nathaniel Hawthorne

232

"But what is happiness except the simple
harmony between a man and the life he leads?"

– Albert Camus

233

"Make space in your life for the things that
matter, for family and friends, love and
generosity, fun and joy. Without this, you
will burn out in mid-career and wonder
where your life went."

– Jonathan Sacks

234

"It is only in sorrow bad weather masters
us; in joy we face the storm and defy it."

– Amelia Barr

235

"Happiness does not lie in happiness,
but in the achievement of it."

– Fyodor Dostoevsky

236

"The deeper the blue becomes, the more strongly it calls man towards the infinite, awakening in him a desire for the pure and, finally, for the supernatural... The brighter it becomes, the more it loses its sound, until it turns into silent stillness and becomes white."

– Wassily Kandinsky

237

"A single rose can be my garden... a single friend, my world."

– Leo Buscaglia

238

"We are what we think. All that we are arises with our thoughts. With our thoughts, we make the world."

– Buddha

239

"We are not victims of aging, sickness
and death. These are part of scenery,
not the seer, who is immune to any form
of change. This seer is the spirit, the
expression of eternal being."

– Deepak Chopra

240

"Nature's music is never over; her silences
are pauses, not conclusions."

– Mary Webb

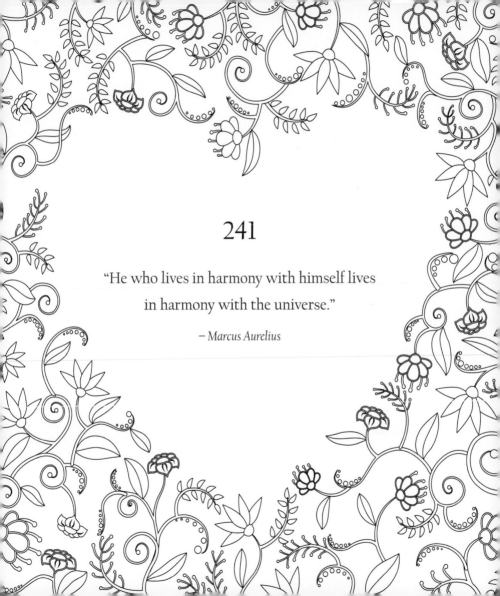

241

"He who lives in harmony with himself lives
in harmony with the universe."

– *Marcus Aurelius*

242

"Love does not consist in gazing at each
other, but in looking outward together
in the same direction."

– Antoine de Saint-Exupéry

243

"Nature is wont to hide herself."

– Heraclitus

244

"Beauty is that which is simultaneously
attractive and sublime."

– Karl Wilhelm Friedrich Schlegel

245

"What art offers is space - a certain
breathing room for the spirit."

– John Updike

246

"If you carry joy in your heart,
you can heal any moment."

– Carlos Santana

247

"Our happiness depends
on wisdom all the way."

– Sophocles

248

"To be without some of the things you want
is an indispensable part of happiness."

— *Bertrand Russell*

249

"Do not speak of your happiness
to one less fortunate than yourself."

— *Plutarch*

250

"The tree which moves some to tears of joy
is in the eyes of others only a green thing
that stands in the way. Some see nature all
ridicule and deformity... and some scarce
see nature at all. But to the eyes of the man
of imagination, nature is imagination itself."

— *William Blake*

251

"Since you get more joy out of giving joy to others, you should put
a good deal of thought into the happiness that you are able to give."

– Eleanor Roosevelt

252

"Beauty is the only thing that time cannot harm. Philosophies fall away
like sand, creeds follow one another, but what is beautiful is a joy for
all seasons, a possession for all eternity."

– Oscar Wilde

253

"Action may not always bring happiness; but there is no
happiness without action."

– Benjamin Disraeli

254

"When meeting difficult situations, one should
dash forward bravely and with joy."

– Yamamoto Tsunetomo

255

"A man's friendships are one of the best
measures of his worth."

– Charles Darwin

256

"There is something terribly morbid in the modern sympathy with pain.
One should sympathise with the color, the beauty, the joy of life.
The less said about life's sores the better."

– Oscar Wilde

257

"Blue is the male principle, stern and spiritual. Yellow the female principle,
gentle, cheerful and sensual. Red is matter, brutal and heavy and always
the color which must be fought and vanquished by the other two."

– Franz Marc

258

"Each blade of grass has its spot on earth whence it draws its life,
its strength; and so is man rooted to the land from which he draws
his faith together with his life."

– Joseph Conrad

"You know it's love when all you want is that person to be happy, even if you're not part of their happiness."

– *Julia Roberts*

"I know the joy of fishes in the river through my own joy, as I go walking along the same river."

– *Zhuangzi*

261

"Things are not quite so simple always
as black and white."

– *Doris Lessing*

262

"A friend is what the heart needs
all the time."

– Henry van Dyke

263

"The person born with a talent they
are meant to use will find their greatest
happiness in using it."

– Johann Wolfgang von Goethe

264

"Human spirit is the ability to face
the uncertainty of the future with
curiosity and optimism. It is the
belief that problems can be
solved, differences resolved.
It is a type of confidence.
And it is fragile. It can be
blackened by fear
and superstition."

– Bernard Beckett

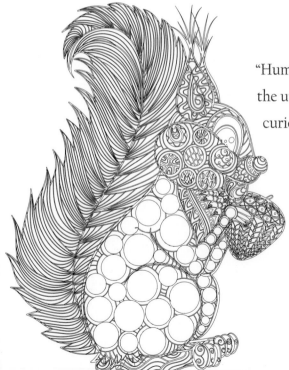

265

"Beauty in things exists in the mind
which contemplates them."

– David Hume

266

"Nature, like man, sometimes weeps
from gladness."

– Benjamin Disraeli

267

"Happiness is like those palaces in fairy
tales whose gates are guarded by dragons:
we must fight in order to conquer it."

– Alexandre Dumas

268

"Be content to seem what you really are."

— *Marcus Aurelius*

269

"The happiness of a man in this life does
not consist in the absence but in the
mastery of his passions."

— *Alfred Tennyson*

270

"Money has never made man happy, nor
will it; there is nothing in its nature to
produce happiness. The more of it one
has the more one wants."

— *Benjamin Franklin*

271

"Through a painting we can
see the whole world."

– *Hans Hofmann*

272

"Find ecstasy in life; the mere
sense of living is joy enough."

– *Emily Dickinson*

273

"I discovered that if one looks a little
closer at this beautiful world, there
are always red ants underneath."

– *David Lynch*

274

"Happiness can only be found if you can
free yourself of all other distractions."

– Saul Bellow

275

"If you smile when no one else is around,

you really mean it."

– *Andy Rooney*

276

"We live in a wonderful world that is full of beauty, charm and adventure. There is no end to the adventures that we can have if only we seek them with our eyes open."

– Jawaharlal Nehru

277

"Friendship... is not something you learn in school. But if you haven't learned the meaning of friendship, you really haven't learned anything."

– Muhammad Ali

278

"I have drunken deep of joy, and I will taste
no other wine tonight."

– Percy Bysshe Shelley

279

"Observe constantly that all things take place
by change, and accustom thyself to consider
that the nature of the Universe loves nothing
so much as to change the things which are,
and to make new things like them."

– Marcus Aurelius

280

"Sorrows gather around great souls as storms do
around mountains; but, like them, they break the
storm and purify the air of the plain beneath them."

– Jean Paul

281

"Happy he who learns to bear
what he cannot change."

– *Friedrich Schiller*

282

"Red is the ultimate cure for sadness."

– Bill Blass

283

"When the past no longer illuminates
the future, the spirit walks in darkness."

– Alexis de Tocqueville

284

"We shall never know all the good
that a simple smile can do."

– Mother Teresa of Calcutta

285

"There is a kind of beauty in imperfection."

– Conrad Hall

286

"Even in the centuries which appear to us
to be the most monstrous and foolish, the
immortal appetite for beauty has always
found satisfaction."

– Charles Baudelaire

287

"Every flower is a soul blossoming in nature."

– *Gérard de Nerval*

288

"To the artist there is never anything ugly in nature."

– *Auguste Rodin*

289

"Man was born free, and he is everywhere in chains."

– *Jean-Jacques Rousseau*

290

"Life is neither good or evil, but only
a place for good and evil."

– *Marcus Aurelius*

291

"Happiness seems made to be shared."

– *Pierre Corneille*

292

"To find joy in work is to discover
the fountain of youth."

– *Pearl S. Buck*

293

"True friendship multiplies the good in life and divides its evils.
Strive to have friends, for life without friends is like life on a
desert island... to find one real friend in a lifetime is good fortune;
to keep him is a blessing."

– Baltasar Gracian

294

"A thing of beauty is a joy forever:
its loveliness increases; it will never
pass into nothingness."

– John Keats

295

"Happiness is neither without us nor within us.
It is in God, both without us and within us."

– Blaise Pascal

296

"I love those who can smile in trouble, who can gather strength from distress, and grow brave by reflection. 'Tis the business of little minds to shrink, but they whose heart is firm, and whose conscience approves their conduct, will pursue their principles unto death."

– *Leonardo da Vinci*

297

"Exuberance is beauty."

– *William Blake*

298

"Be content with what you are, and wish not change; nor dread your last day, nor long for it."

– *Marcus Aurelius*

299

"The time for action is now. It's never too late to do something."

— Antoine de Saint-Exupéry

300

"I long remained a child, and I am still one in many respects."

— Jean-Jacques Rousseau

301

"Happiness is good health and a bad memory."

— Ingrid Bergman

302

"Grief can take care of itself, but to get the full value of a joy you must have somebody to divide it with."

– *Mark Twain*

303

"Culture is the widening of the mind and of the spirit."

– *Jawaharlal Nehru*

304

"Smile in the mirror. Do that every morning and you'll start to see a big difference in your life."

– *Yoko Ono*

305

"I think luck is the sense to recognize
an opportunity and the ability to take
advantage of it... The man who can smile
at his breaks and grab his chances gets on."

– Samuel Goldwyn

306

"Beauty is in the heart of the beholder."

– H. G. Wells

307

"Art requires philosophy, just as philosophy
requires art. Otherwise, what would
become of beauty?"

– Paul Gauguin

308

"Nature does not hurry,
yet everything is accomplished."

– Lao Tzu

309

"It is the chiefest point of happiness
that a man is willing to be what he is."

– Erasmus of Rotterdam

310

"The ineffable joy of forgiving and being
forgiven forms an ecstasy that might well
arouse the envy of the gods."

– Elbert Hubbard

311

"Rare as is true love,
true friendship is rarer."

– *Jean de La Fontaine*

312

"If you want to accomplish the goals of your
life, you have to begin with the spirit."

– *Oprah Winfrey*

313

"Nobility of spirit has more to do with
simplicity than ostentation, wisdom rather than
wealth, commitment rather than ambition."

– *Riccardo Muti*

314

"Smile, it's free therapy."

– Douglas Horton

315

"Indeed it is possible to stand with one foot on the inevitable 'banana peel' of life with both eyes peering into the Great Beyond, and still be happy, comfortable, and serene - if we will even so much as smile."

– Douglas Fairbanks

316

"It is amazing how complete is the delusion that beauty is goodness."

– Leo Tolstoy

317

"We ought to do good to others as simply as a horse runs,
or a bee makes honey, or a vine bears grapes season after season
without thinking of the grapes it has borne."

– Marcus Aurelius

318

"Wear a smile and have friends;

wear a scowl and have wrinkles."

– George Eliot

319

"A friend is someone who gives you
total freedom to be yourself."

— *Jim Morrison*

320

"To live according to the spirit is to love
according to the spirit."

– *Saint Francis de Sales*

321

"Our most intimate friend is not he to whom we show the worst, but the best of our nature."

– *Nathaniel Hawthorne*

322

"All happiness or unhappiness solely depends upon the quality of the object to which we are attached by love."

– *Baruch Spinoza*

323

"The real man smiles in trouble, gathers strength from distress, and grows brave by reflection."

– *Thomas Paine*

324

"Be as a tower firmly set; shakes not its top for any blast that blows."

– Dante Alighieri

325

"Nothing has such power to broaden the mind as the ability to investigate systematically and truly all that comes under thy observation in life."

– Marcus Aurelius

326

"Autumn is a second spring when every leaf is a flower."

– Albert Camus

327

"You can't really say what is beautiful about
a place, but the image of the place will
remain vividly with you."

– Tadao Ando

328

"Anything you're good at contributes
to happiness."

– Bertrand Russell

329

"After every storm the sun will smile;
for every problem there is a solution,
and the soul's indefeasible duty is to
be of good cheer."

– William R. Alger

330

"The main thing that you have to remember
on this journey is, just be nice to everyone
and always smile."

– *Ed Sheeran*

331

"Let not your mind run on what you lack
as much as on what you have already."

– *Marcus Aurelius*

332

"Nature never deceives us;
it is we who deceive ourselves."

– *Jean-Jacques Rousseau*

333

"What the caterpillar calls the end
of the world the master calls a butterfly."

– Richard Bach

334

"We may brave human laws, but we cannot resist natural ones."

– Jules Verne

335

"Desire nothing, give up all desires and be happy."

– Swami Sivananda

336

"Despair is the damp of hell, as joy is the serenity of heaven."

– John Donne

337

"Happiness, true happiness, is an inner quality. It is a state of mind. If your mind is at peace, you are happy. If your mind is at peace, but you have nothing else, you can be happy. If you have everything the world can give - pleasure, possessions, power - but lack peace of mind, you can never be happy."

– Dada Vaswani

338

"In the depth of winter I finally learned that there was in me an invincible summer."

– Albert Camus

339

"Everyone chases after happiness, not noticing
that happiness is right at their heels."

– Bertolt Brecht

340

"We will be more successful in all our endeavors
if we can let go of the habit of running all
the time, and take little pauses to relax and
re-center ourselves. And we'll also have
a lot more joy in living."

– Thich Nhat Hanh

341

"If you have one true friend you
have more than your share."

– Thomas Fuller

342

"Freedom is the open window through which pours the sunlight
of the human spirit and human dignity."

– Herbert Hoover

343

"Research has shown that the best way to be happy
is to make each day happy."

– Deepak Chopra

344

"Time is a sort of river of passing events, and strong is its current;
no sooner is a thing brought to sight than it is swept by and another
takes its place, and this too will be swept away."

– Marcus Aurelius

345

"The advantage of the emotions
is that they lead us astray."

– Oscar Wilde

346

"I know but one freedom,
and that is the freedom of the mind."

– Antoine de Saint-Exupéry

347

"Beauty is produced by the pleasing
appearance and good taste of the whole,
and by the dimensions of all the parts being
duly proportioned to each other."

– Vitruvius

348

"Our task must be to free ourselves by
widening our circle of compassion to
embrace all living creatures and the whole
of nature and its beauty."

– Albert Einstein

349

"When I admire the wonders of a sunset
or the beauty of the moon, my soul expands
in the worship of the creator."

– Mahatma Gandhi

350

"Your successes and happiness are forgiven you
only if you generously consent to share them."

– Albert Camus

351

"I believe enlightenment or revelation comes in daily life. I look for joy, the peace of action. You need action. I'd have stopped writing years ago if it were for the money."

– Paulo Coelho

352

"Friends are born, not made."

– Henry Adams

353

"Smiling is definitely one of the best beauty remedies. If you have a good sense of humor and a good approach to life, that's beautiful."

– Rashida Jones

354

"The happiness of life is made up of minute fractions - the little, soon forgotten charities of a kiss or a smile, a kind look or heartfelt compliment."

– Samuel Taylor Coleridge

355

"I would feel more optimistic about a bright future for man if he spent less time proving that he can outwit Nature and more time tasting her sweetness and respecting her seniority."

– E. B. White

356

"Think of all the beauty still left around you and be happy."

– Anne Frank

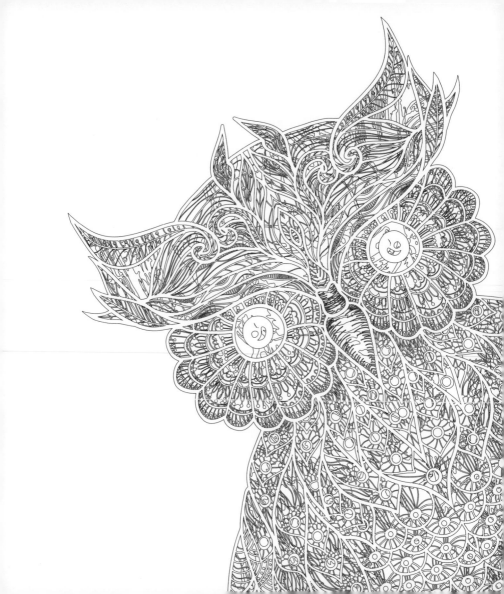

357

"Happiness resides not in possessions, and not in gold, happiness dwells in the soul."

— Democritus

358

"True silence is the rest of the mind, and is to the spirit what sleep is to the body, nourishment and refreshment."

— William Penn

359

"Off with you! You're a happy fellow, for you'll give happiness and joy to many other people. There is nothing better or greater than that!"

— Ludwig van Beethoven

360

"Children learn to smile from their parents."

– *Shinichi Suzuki*

361

"Beauty of whatever kind, in its supreme
development, invariably excites
the sensitive soul to tears."

– *Edgar Allan Poe*

362

"Just living is not enough... one must have sunshine,
freedom, and a little flower."

– *Hans Christian Andersen*

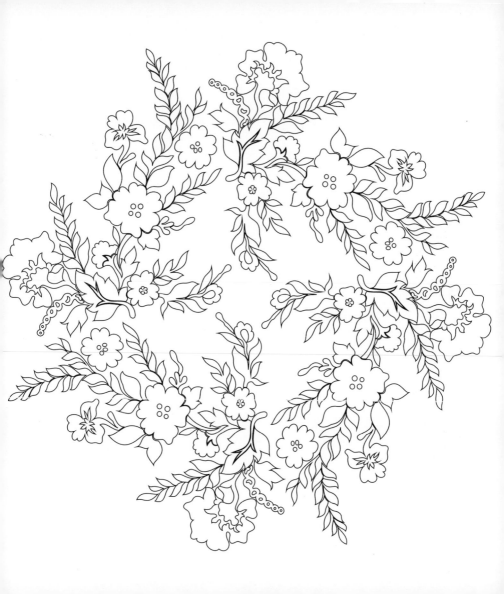

363

"There are always flowers for those
who want to see them."

– Henri Matisse

364

"Sunset is still my favorite color,
and rainbow is second."

– Mattie Stepanek

365

"Mother Nature is always speaking. She speaks in a language understood within the peaceful mind of the sincere observer. Leopards, cobras, monkeys, rivers and trees; they all served as my teachers when I lived as a wanderer in the Himalayan foothills."

– Radhanath Swami

List of contributors

Illustration Credits

All illustrations are reworkings of images drawn
from 123RF, iStockphoto and Shutterstock

Graphic design

Paola Piacco

vmb Publishers® is a registered trademark
property of De Agostini Libri S.p.A.

© 2016 De Agostini Libri S.p.A.
Via G. da Verrazano, 15 - 28100 Novara, Italy
www.whitestar.it - www.deagostini.it

ISBN 978-88-540-3284-2
1 2 3 4 5 6   20 19 18 17 16

Printed in China